C0-ANZ-188

FUNNY FABLES OF FUNDY

AND OTHER POEMS FOR CHILDREN

WRITTEN AND ILLUSTRATED

BY

GRACE HELEN MOWAT

Print'N Press Ltd., St. Stephen, N. B.

FUNNY FABLES OF FUNDY

by

Grace Helen Mowat

First published by Ru-Mi-Lou Books, Ottawa. Republished in 1977 by Print'N Press Ltd., St. Stephen, N. B.

THIRD PRINTING 1984
By Print'N Press Ltd., St. Stephen, N. B.

ISBN 0-920732-02-X

INTRODUCTION

This nostalgic little book of poems, written and illustrated for children by Grace Helen Mowat, was first published in 1928. The childhood models for some of the drawings are today adults in St. Andrews.

Grace Helen Mowat was something of a legend in her own time. Born in St. Andrews in 1875, she was the only child of strongly Loyalist parents. A lonely childhood served to sharpen her powers of observation and develop her imagination; she was to identify readily with children all her life.

After receiving art training at the Cooper Union in New York "Nellie" Mowat taught for a time at the Ladies' College of Art in Halifax, N. S. She was, however, drawn back to her home by the sea where her real life's work was to begin.

She wrote poetry, novels and a history of her town ("The Diverting History of a Loyalist Town" is still in demand) - she started a small pottery and she established Charlotte County Cottage Craft, a cottage industry which continues to this day.

As if this weren't enough, she founded the Music, Art and Drama Club which is still in existence. "Spinning Wheel Song" (p. 67) was written for one of the Farmers' Pageants which she organized and staged in one of the fields near her house at the Mowat Farm.

Some of these poems are more than fables, they are allegories relating to actual persons and events ("Jim Crow and his Wife" "Bird Law") in which she poked fun at human frailties.

Honoured for her many talents and contributions to the life of the Province, she was awarded an honorary Doctor of Laws degree by the University of New Brunswick in 1951. Dr. Grace Helen Mowat died in February 1964, a well-loved and respected citizen of her Loyalist Town.

St. Andrews Civic Trust Inc. expresses its sincere appreciation to Margaret Everett Hilditch, second cousin of the author, who has granted permission to the Trust to republish this work.

CONTENTS

PROLOGUE

Fables, my child, to you are told,
To make you wise when you are old.
They have a moral at the end,
(To which I hope you will attend)
And learn thus to avoid mistakes,
Observing those another makes.
In such a manner Æsop speaks,
Admonishing the ancient Greeks.
But, just for that, you need not cry:
"Oh dear! how very dull and dry!"
For in these fables, every one,
You'll find a fund of Fundy fun.

DEDICATION

(To Mr. William Brodie, my old school-master)

For the school days, long since fled,
For the wayward class you led,
With the pointer in your hand,
Into paths of Fable-land;
Tracing joys that never cease
On a map of ancient Greece.
Athens—Sparta—Arcady—
Marathon—Thermopylæ.
In that faded map we saw,
With gods from out Olympia,
Trojan heroes, warrior kings,
Fauns and nymphs and fabled things
That, in pageantry grotesque,
Circled round my ink-stained desk.
For these things you taught to me
In the old academy.
Take my Fable Book, the same
As wildflowers brought for you to name,
And for the reckless things I dared,
And for all lessons unprepared,
Lessons that I failed to know
More than thirty years ago,
May this little book amend—
Teacher, oracle and friend.

Oh, happy Bay of Fundy; for there for evermore,
Children find their fairy lands beside its lovely shore!

THE BAY OF FUNDY

I like the Bay of Fundy,
Where tides creep up the strand,
With driftwood for the fire,
And rockweed for the land.
From Yarmouth to Chignecto, around and back again,
They reach the Quoddy Islands and wash the shores of
      Maine.

I like the Bay of Fundy,
Where sandstone Islands wait
The rosy kiss of sunset,
Beside the western gate.
And up the inland rivers, that seek the Fundy tides,
A pleasant land of apple trees and happy homes
      abides.

I like the Bay of Fundy—
For when the tide is out,
So many wonders of the deep
Are scattered all about.
Oh, happy Bay of Fundy; for there for evermore,
Children find their fairy lands beside its lovely shore!

THE FROG POND

Father Frog was very sad,
Sitting on a lily pad.

Mother Frog, in deepest grief,
Wept upon a bullrush leaf.

Grandpa Frog, upon a stone,
Sat in silence all alone.

And the cause of their distress,
Was their children's waywardness.

Thus you see the elder frogs—
In come naughty pollywogs.

Mother questions through her tears:
"Why, where have you been, my dears?"

"Dancing," said the pollywogs,
"At the phosphorescent bogs."

Father grumbled: " 'Tisn't right!
Children should be home at night!"

Mother said: "At any rate,
You should not remain so late."

"Dear, we couldn't leave the thing
Till they played 'God Save the King'."

THE FROG POND—*Continued*

Mother (having lost her rest),
Rather failed to be impressed.

"What about your tails?" she sobbed.
"Mother dear, we had them bobbed."

Father Frog said: "In my day,
Children did not act this way."

Said the children: "Poor old Dad!
Think what fun you might have had!"

Grandpa Frog, in croaky tone,
Said: "Come, gather round this stone."

All the pollywogs obeyed.
"Grandpa's an old dear," they said.

"Children," said the aged Frog,
"I was once a pollywog

"Just as young and gay as you—
Though I now am ninety-two.

"You, who now are pollywogs,
Some day will be aged frogs.

"It is well to look ahead.
Now, my children, go to bed!"

THE FROG POND—*Continued.*

Swimming off when they were sent,
Well they knew what Grandpa meant.

And they whispered as they swum:
"He will settle Dad and Mum!"

Turning to the puzzled pair,
Grandpa said: "Now, don't you care,

"By these children I can tell,
That I brought you up too well.

Grandpa Frog, in croaky tone,
Said: "Come, gather round this stone."

THE FROG POND—*Concluded*

"When these children older grow,
By experience they will know

"How to settle pollywogs
Who dance in phosphorescent bogs."

MORAL:

The moral here is quite obscure,
But you can find it out, I'm sure,

And learn (as all wise children should)
To know the evil from the good;

So in the coming generation
You'll be a blessing to the nation.

JIM CROW AND HIS WIFE

Jim Crow selected for his use
The top branch of the tallest spruce.

Said he to his wife Arabel:
"I think that we have chosen well.

"We will have pleasant neighbours here,
And well-stocked corn-fields very near.

"I feel that all is for the best—
So let us start to build our nest."

They worked together, bill to bill,
And plied their trade with wondrous skill.

And when they viewed their home complete,
It looked extremely trim and neat.

"I wish, Jim dear," said Mrs. Crow,
"That we could have a radio.

"The hen-hawk has been telling me
That you could make one easily;

"With wire and a bit of string,
A wooden box or anything.

"Constructed with intelligence,
Would give us one at small expense.

JIM CROW AND HIS WIFE—*Continued*.

"The radio, I've often heard,
  Is so instructive for a bird.

"For one thing we could hear, I'm sure,
  The orioles of Baltimore.

"And what an operatic treat,
  To listen to a parakeet!

"Some useful items we might gain,
  Hearing reports about the grain.

"Then how our fledglings would delight
  In bed-time stories told at night!

"I wish, dear, you would have a talk
  With this most interesting hawk."

  Then Jim said: "Well, it's up to me,
  To show a crow's sagacity.

"So now while it is pleasant weather,
  I'll get material together.

"I know a tangled wire fence—
  And that is where I will commence.

"Already I have formed some plans
  For ear-phones made from sardine cans."

JIM CROW AND HIS WIFE—*Continued*.

Next day, with confidence immense,
He went to seek the wire fence.

Finding the staples hard to pull
He called out to a passing bull:

"Just pull these staples out," said he,
"They come a little hard for me."

The bull enquired, with a roar:
"What are you using wire for?"

And Jim said: "Well, my wife, you know,
Wants me to make a radio."

At that the bull gave such a roar,
The farmer's wife came to the door.

And seeing Jim, she called her son
Requesting him to bring a gun.

Poor Jim a place of safety sought,
And trembling heard the loud report.

Escaping barely with his life,
Flew swiftly home to tell his wife.

Arabel thought it would be best
To be more cautious in his quest.

The hen-hawk, who dropped in one night,
Told Jim he had not made it right.

JIM CROW AND HIS WIFE—*Continued*

Thus, day by day, with patient toil,
And danger, trouble and turmoil,

Jim laboured to complete his plans,
With ear-phones made from sardine cans;

But nothing came in very clear
That he and Arabel could hear.

The hen-hawk, who dropped in one night,
Told Jim he had not made it right.

Said he: "The thing will never go,
Without a battery, you know."

And Jim exclaimed: "Why, to be sure,
I should have thought of that before!"

And Arabel said prettily:
"We are such amateurs, you see.

"Now do explain to Jim and me,
What constitutes a battery."

The hawk said: "Now I am not sure,
(Being myself an amateur),

"But really now it seems to me
Batter should make a battery."

JIM CROW AND HIS WIFE—*Continued*

"Just take some batter," said the hawk,
"And treat it with a little chalk,

"Then let it harden over night,
And there's your battery, all right.

"A lady here, named Miss McPhee,
Makes batter every night for tea.

"I know her chicken yard—in short,
I've been there for a little sport—

"Just state the reason why you came,
But tactfully avoid my name."

Jim, in a note book, carefully
Put down the name of Miss McPhee.

And, having ascertained the way,
Set off to find the place next day.

Now when at last the house he saw
He hopped right through the open door,

And there inside was Miss McPhee,
Mixing the batter for her tea.

Said Jim: "This is the place, I think,"
And hopped upon the kitchen sink.

JIM CROW AND HIS WIFE—*Continued*

Said Jim: "This is the place, I think,"
And hopped upon the kitchen sink.

Said Miss McPhee: "What is the matter?
You almost made me spill the batter."

Said Jim: "Give me some batter, please,
I want to make some batteries."

"Upon my word," said Miss McPhee,
"This crow will be the death of me!"

JIM CROW AND HIS WIFE—*Continued*

"I need a battery," said the crow,
"To make my wife a radio."

But Miss McPhee had never heard
About a battery for a bird;

"So now," said she, "You'd better go—
I always did despise a crow."

Jim's temper rose, he lost control,
And madly flew into the bowl.

As helplessly he flopped around,
He greatly feared he would be drowned.

Cried Miss McPhee: "You lunatic!
Take that"—and whacked him with a stick.

"A pretty battery now are you!"
And out the window Jim she threw.

Into a nearby burdock bed,
Jim fell upon his aching head.

With burrs and batter covered quite,
He found himself in sorry plight.

Rising in pain from where he fell,
He limped back home to Arabel.

JIM CROW AND HIS WIFE—*Continued*

She cleaned him up beside the sink
And gave him crocus tea to drink.

She tied a bandage round his head
And put him in a feather bed.

When Jim had told to Arabel
The dreadful things he had to tell,

She said to him: "My dearest crow,
I do not want a radio!

"To-night the hermit thrush I heard—
More sweet than any foreign bird.

"To live content without a care;
To have the freedom of the air;

"To swing upon the spruce tree's crest,
To own a comfortable nest—

"Is better for the race of crows,
Than a whole world of radios.

"That hawk is often most unwise,
Although he thinks he can advise.

"I do not think the average crow
Should bother with a radio."

JIM CROW AND HIS WIFE—*Concluded*

And poor Jim wiped away a tear
And said: "I'm sure of that, my dear."

MORAL:

There is no harm in radios:
That is not what the moral shows.
But if you study what befell
The plans of Jim and Arabel,
Then you will see, if you are wise,
How very well the tale applies.
To those who like to take a hand,
In things they do not understand;
So don't be guided by the talk
Of every bold and foolish hawk.

JERSEY LILY

In the lovely summer weather
Jersey Lily broke her tether;
Called upon the milkman's herd.
(Really Lily was absurd).
Then went on towards the town
Stopped to call on Farmer Brown.
Farmer Brown said: "How d'yer do,"
Lily only answered "Moo-o-o."
Farmer Brown, with two large jugs,
Went to kill potato bugs;
When he spilled the Paris green
Lily licked the place up clean.
When she came back home that night,
She had lost her appetite.
Could not tempt her with a treat;
Dainties she refused to eat.
With the dawning of the day
Lily gently slept away.
Farmer Brown came up to see:
"Looks quite natural, too," said he;
"Wish the day had never been,
  That I bought that Paris green!"
Underneath the hawthorn bough,
There we laid our pretty cow.
There I let the clover grow—
Lily always loved it so.
Lily's little Jersey calf
Helped me write this epitaph:

JERSEY LILY—*Continued.*

Just the simple facts we wrote;
Reading from the stone, I quote:
"Broken tether—Paris green—
Jersey Lily—no more seen!"

The moral here is very plain—
I hardly think I need explain.

THE TIDES

A stranger once said to the tides in the Bay:
"How strange you should live in this indolent way;
You crawl up the strand and then crawl down again
Why can't you be useful and helpful to men?
For the past thousand years you have been just the same,
Such an idle existence!   It's really a shame!"

The tides, rather ruffled, cried "What do you wish?
We fill up the fish weirs and bring in the fish
And drift-wood and rock-weed and much else besides,
Why, everyone waits for the turn of the tides!
We've washed the shores clean and never once shirked
If you did half as much you would feel overworked!"

"I propose," said the stranger (ignoring their theme),
"To use all your strength in a practical scheme.
I studied at college before I came here,
And everyone thinks me a great engineer!
I can hardly expect you to know who I am,
But I'm seriously thinking of building a dam
To keep you in bounds, till I need you, of course,
And then I expect to control you by force.
You can turn wheels and cranks by this simple device
And greatly aid commerce.   Now won't that be nice?"

The waves made no answer to what the man said;
But talking it over that evening in bed

THE TIDES—*Continued*

They grumbled and murmured: "We need not fear him;
Beside our great strength his adventure looks slim.
If he build up this dam, it is perfectly plain,
We must all push together and break it again.
And, if this arrangement should fail to survive,
We can wash in a shark that will eat him alive!"

The engineer tactfully waited awhile
Then, appearing next morning, he said with a smile:
"Dear tides, I am taking a trip up to town,
I hope you need something that I can bring down?"

They haughtily said: "You may bring, if you wish,
Some good gelatine for the young jelly-fish."

The item he added at once to his list,
And spoke of returning before he was missed;
And just as he promised, came home the next night,
His pockets all bulging with plans, blue and white,
The gelatine too he remembered to bring,
(For jelly-fish need it so much in the spring!)
"These plans," he explained, "will bring gold to your
                shore
By giving employment to men by the score."
But the tides in a voice that was hollow and cold,
Said: "Our fishes are silver; we don't care for gold."
"How hopelessly dull," cried the great engineer.
"My college diploma is little use here!

3

THE TIDES—*Continued*

I cannot express how this talk makes me feel!"
And appearing quite angry, he turned on his heel.

Then sea-gulls brought word that a numerous band
Of workmen were filling the channel with sand,
And talked of erecting a barrier so high,
That no tides could cross over unless they could fly.

"Very well," said the tides, "let him do as he will,
And we for a time will keep perfectly still
And wait for the Equinox gales in the Fall—
And then you will see what becomes of this wall!"

The sea-gulls that Autumn all gathered in flocks,
To await the return of the fall Equinox.
They were fighting for seats with the plovers and crows,
When all of a sudden the Equinox rose!

With rushing and roaring the tides came apace—
And dealt the great structure a slap in the face!

The engineer, viewing the frantic attack,
Admonished the tides that they better keep back!
But they cried, "We are holding our annual ball,
When the Equinox comes for a dance in the fall."

Then the tides with fantastic grimaces upreared,
And the engineer groaned, "It is just as I feared!"

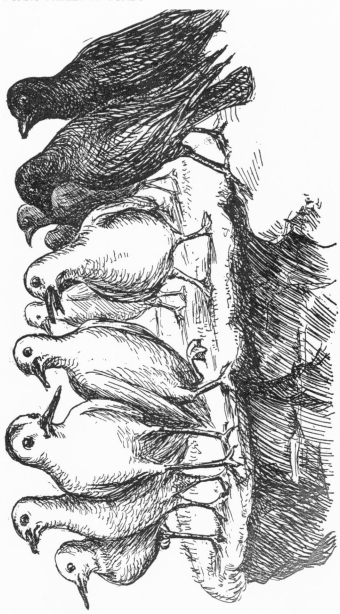

They were fighting for seats with the plovers and crows,
When all of a sudden the Equinox rose!

THE TIDES—*Concluded*

Down, down, went the dam and the sea-wall besides,
And the engineer fell with the wreck in the tides.
And the waves washed his pockets as clean as could be
And carried his plans and his gold out to sea.

He may have survived, for I know he could swim,
But the tides never more have been bothered with him.

MORAL:

These facts tell us plainly to look on all sides
Before we are tempted to tamper with tides;
And when we are strangers, wherever we go,
There's always a side that we still do not know;
And if we too suddenly start to reform
Our plans and our gold may be lost in the storm!

BIRD LAW

A swallow once left in the charge of a jay
Her nest in the rafters when she went away;
And, on her returning, one lovely spring morn,
She found all her treasures were stolen and gone.

The swallow then called on the jay at her home,
And found there her treasures adorning the room.
The jay, feeling guilty, and rather afraid,
Explained she was sure a mistake had been made.
She felt much insulted, but wiping her eyes,
Resolved in her mind to invent a few lies.

The swallow applied to a magistrate bird,
And besought that in counsel her case might be heard.
But the clerk of the peace was a timorous snail,
Who crawled in his shell upon hearing the tale,
For, said he: "I fear greatly all order would cease,
If the swallow should swallow the clerk of the peace."

In hope of concealment the jay very soon
Sought to feather her nest with the help of the loon,
For the loon, she decided, might enter the game,
If aroused by suspicion about her good name.

Now the loon, although stupid, was rich as could be
And had built her a very grand house by the sea.
A small English sparrow she had for a spouse,
Though she let it be known that it was not his house.

BIRD LAW—*Continued*

When the jay saw the loon she asked if she knew
That the swallow was spreading a tale most untrue;
How the loon at a party had drunk too much ale—
And some were believing the scandalous tale?
And then added weeping: "I've not told the whole!
This villainous bird is now saying I stole!"

The loon called her husband, on hearing this tale,
And said she would certainly try and prevail
On the judge and the jury and tell them to say
They could not find anything wrong with the jay.

"My word," said the sparrow, "how nice of you, dear!
I'm sure you can easily get the jay clear;
And people will say as they pass by our door
The sparrow and loon are so good to the poor!"

In the court room assembled were all kinds of fowl.
The jury were wild geese, the judge was an owl,
And the jay and the loon had engaged for defence
A woodpecker lawyer with learning immense.

The loon told the owl, as she drew him aside,
That she knew for a fact that the swallow had lied.
"The jay is not guilty of this evil deed!
She says so herself! What more proof do you need?
And likewise, your Honour, from what I have heard,
This swallow is really a dangerous bird!

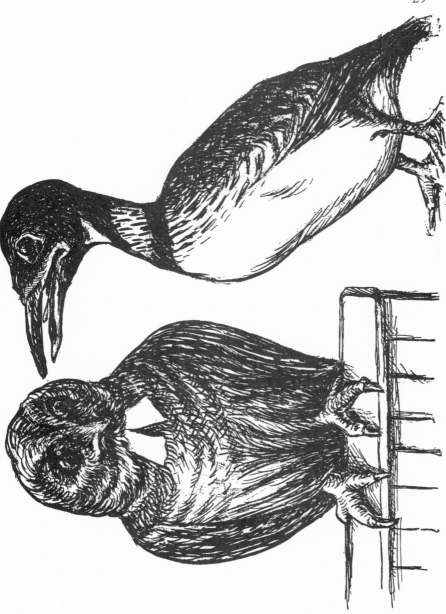

The loon told the owl, as she drew him aside,
That she knew for a fact that the swallow had lied.

BIRD LAW—*Continued*

She has said on account of my laughter,—that's all,
That I took too much ale at the sand-pipers' ball."

"Dear Loon," said the owl, "your gay laughter to me
Is sweet as the sugar I take in my tea;
And if this unfortunate jay is your friend,
I surely will see that her troubles soon end.

"I like to be kind, and a bird of my age
Should avoid shutting other birds up in a cage.
I often see fit to obscure a rash deed,
When in judgment I sit.   Let proceedings proceed!"

The woodpecker, rising, then tried to expound
That the case of the swallow was quite without ground.
"Consider," said he, "all the birds of the air—
Yet you blame this poor jay!   Do you think it is fair?"

The swallow replied that she truly could say
The goods had been found in the house of the jay.
But the woodpecker argued that often a guest
Had been asked by the swallow to visit her nest;
And goods by such guests might be stolen away,
And sold or presented by them to the jay.

A similar case had once happened before:
He could quote from a section on page fifty-four.
The jay was not guilty of what had been done,
And so said her husband and so said her son.

BIRD LAW—*Continued*

The benevolent loon had gone out of her way
To prevail on the jury to pardon the jay.
An intelligent jury undoubtedly sees
We are serving the public and aiming to please!

But the jury were dreaming of soft feather beds,
And under their wings had disposed of their heads:
And a crow in the doorway disdainfully cawed:
"I'm sure it's no wonder the jury are bored;
And I, at a venture, would strongly suspect,
The tree was quite hollow that woodpecker pecked."

The martin, who also stood back in the crowd,
Replied: "That is true, but don't say it so loud!
The loon has got money that might come my way,
So I want her to think that I side with the jay."

The owl then addressing the court said: "I think
It is time to go home, I'm beginning to blink.
I cannot have any more witnesses come—
The hour grows late and I want to go home.
So wake up the jury, and tell them to say
They cannot find anything wrong with the jay!"

The loon, much delighted, declared without fail
That the judge must come home for a glass of pale ale.
A bootlegger's craft had been wrecked close at hand,
And a case from the cargo was hid in the sand;

BIRD LAW—*Continued*

The owl after sipping his glass said: "This ale
Appears, to my thinking, exceedingly pale."

The sparrow said also, on taking a drink,
"It must have been standing too long in the sink."
So the loon told her husband to hop down the strand
And bring back the case that was hid in the sand.

He returned in an hour, remarking "I think,
My love, we won't offer his honour a drink.
That ungrateful jay has run off with the case,
And when I objected she laughed in my face!"

The loon in a panic excitedly raved,
They'd been openly robbed by the bird they had saved!

"Indeed," said the owl,   "I'm beginning to see,
You've been gulled by this jay, and you've tried to gull
          me!
I believe that she lied in the court-room to-day,
And I let her go free!   Oh, what will people say?"

So he flew to the wild wood to hide his regret—
And for all that I know he is living there yet.

BIRD LAW—*Concluded*

MORAL:

Now, children, be warned by this tale, which is true,
The swallow told me and I tell it to you.
For the men of to-morrow are children to-day—
So when you grow up, please recall what I say.
You cannot have safety and justice and peace,
With an owl for a judge and a jury of geese.
And if you want help when enforcing the law,
Beware of a loon that's protecting the poor!

THE CONTENTED TURKEY

An old turkey gobbler once said:
"I have gobbled in farmyard and shed,
    I have gobbled all day,
    Now I find with dismay
That I will be gobbled instead.

"I am sure it is good for the nation,
To give thanks with a great proclamation,
    But for me and my kind,
    Thanksgiving I find
A season of great perturbation."

Said I to the turkey: "Oh, yes,
But you'll be such a social success.
    It never would do
    To give thanks without you—
Though you're sent to the kitchen to dress."

"I hope I won't mind it," he cried.
They will stuff me with chestnuts inside,
    And eat me, of course,
    With some cranberry sauce;
But I may be quite glad that I died."

THE CONTENTED TURKEY—*Concluded*

MORAL:

The moral is plain, is it not?
You can see it right off on the spot.
It shows what is meant
By being content
With any old kind of a lot.

HONEY FOR TEA

When I was young I could not see
How any one could love a bee.
(And yet I 'spose its mother would,
When it was in its babyhood.)
The flowers are sweet, the birds can sing,
But all a bee can do is sting.
I never knew how bad they were
Till one day, walking in the square,
A horrid buzzing bee came by
And stung me just above the eye.
It pained me so I cried aloud,
And that attracted quite a crowd.
They took me to a chemist's shop
And tried to make the aching stop.
They told me I would soon be well,
Although my face began to swell,
Applied witch-hazel and Bay rum;
And called a cab to take me home.
The chemist thinks the same as me
About the habits of the bee.

But in the country (where I go
Sometimes, to visit uncle Jo)
They have a colony of bees
Out underneath the orchard trees,
With houses where the bees can stay—
They pamper them in every way.

Then for my tea I had some bread,
With honey very thickly spread.

So I said when I saw it all,
"I do not like the bees at all."
Said auntie: "Maybe after tea,
You'll change your mind about the bee."
Then for my tea I had some bread,
With honey very thickly spread.
And Auntie said the bees for hours
Collected honey from the flowers,
And brought it all back home for me,

HONEY FOR TEA—*Concluded*

So I could have it for my tea.
So I said: "Auntie, you were right,
I really like the bees to-night."

MORAL:

The moral of all this will show
(At least so says my uncle Jo)
That, though in life there's many a thing
That seems to have a nasty sting,
Yet if we still wait patiently,
The honey will be there for tea.

THE REFUGE

Kind Dr. Moose once made a call on Mrs. Caribou,
Remarking, in a pleasant way: "Good morning, how
    are you?"
And Mrs. Caribou replied: "I've not been well of late,
The hunting season always puts my nerves in such a
    state.
My niece has lost her only son—shot down before her
    eyes!
Her husband, too, from bullet wounds, in great discom-
    fort lies!
Poor Mrs. Deer has also lost her pretty little doe—
All shot and killed by cruel men—and that's the way
    we go!
I hear it said that very soon there'll be no Caribou!"
But cheerful Dr. Moose replied: "I have good news
    for you.
I hear there is a woodland tract that stretches far and
    wide,
And there no cruel men with guns will be allowed in-
    side.
There ample shelter, food and drink are to all creatures
    given."
And Mrs. Caribou replied: "Do you refer to Heaven?"
"Some men who understand our needs," good Dr.
    Moose replied,
"This shelter for all hunted things have kindly set
    aside.
A sign is placed for all to read, with printing nice and
    clear,

4

Kind Dr. Moose once made a call on Mrs. Caribou,
Remarking in a pleasant way: "Good morning, how are you?"

THE REFUGE—*Concluded*

Which says 'PLEASE LEAVE YOUR GUNS OUTSIDE, ALL
      GAME PROTECTED HERE,'
Some men, you know, are not so bad, and I believe it's
      true."
"I don't believe a word of it," said Mrs. Caribou!

MORAL:

Now in this little incident, the moral goes to show
How very trying people are who thus delight in woe.
So if you wish for pleasant friends (and I suppose you
      do),
You'd better be like Dr. Moose than Mrs. Caribou.

BIGGEST AND BEST

The clam, the sea gull and the shark
Were chatting at low water mark.

Finding the conversation flag,
The little clam began to brag.

"I hate," he said, "to hear this talk
Of London, Paris and New York.

"These places, as you well may guess,
Lack many things that I possess.

"Of all the clam flats, East or West,
Mine is the biggest and the best!

"Here I, in this extensive flat,
Have room and bath and things like that.

"I need no feet nor hands nor wings,
They seem extremely useless things.

"I need not move from where I am;
All things come to me," said the clam.

The shark replied, with quick retort,
"You have not any sense of sport!

"Don't think you can compare with *me*,
Who am the terror of the sea.

BIGGEST AND BEST—*Continued*

"I fear no foe, I heed no laws;
  My fame is centered in my jaws.

"Don't talk to me, you stupid clam!"
  And with these words away he swam.

The sea-gull raised her lovely head:
  "They both are in the wrong," she said.

"The clam within his muddy flat
  Sees nothing more in life than that.

"The shark believes his cruel ways
  Will win for him respect and praise.

"But with white wings, where'er I fly,
  I see things greater far than I.

"Greatness was never meant to be
  Measured by size or cruelty.

"The forest vast, the mountain high,
  Are great—but they obscure the sky.

"A star seems just a tiny ray
  Because it shines so far away.

"For me the greatest and the best
  Are my small fledgelings in their nest."

BIGGEST AND BEST—*Concluded*

MORAL:

The sea-gull has the right idea,
Though some would not agree, I fear,
And think, if they outdo the rest,
They are the biggest and the best.
But people talking in this strain
Are often ignorant and vain;
Who, like the clam in muddy flat,
Behold no other world than that.
While others, hoping for applause,
Depend like sharks upon their jaws.

THE DUCK'S DEVICE

Some ducks resided in a shack
Beside the Petitcodiac.
Contentedly they swam and drank
Beside the river's muddy bank;
But in the evening, more afraid,
They slept behind a barricade,
Often receiving nervous shocks
From frequent visits of a fox.
The fox was crafty, old and wise
And by all means he could devise,
Persistently he tried and tried
To get the ducks to come outside;
But always found they were afraid
To come beyond the barricade.
He used to prowl and prowl around
And try to burrow underground.
"Hello there, Mr. Duck!" said he,
"Come out and take a walk with me."
But father told him with a quack
He'd rather stay inside the shack.
The fox, next evening, tried his luck
With flattering words for mother duck,
Saying: "Come out and have a chat:
You are so handsome, large and fat."
But mother duck replied that she
Was not fat like she used to be.
Now all this made the ducks afraid—

Some ducks resided in a shack
Beside the Petitcodiac.

THE DUCK'S DEVICE—*Continued*

Even behind their barricade.
Said brother Bill, the oldest boy:
"I'll teach that fellow to annoy."
But mother duck said: "Dearest son,
There's not a thing that can be done."
And brother Bill said: "Very well—
Only be patient, time will tell."
At length he planned to send the fox
Out sailing in a packing box.
Now Bill, when foraging for meals,
Had often chatted with the eels,
And soon resolved to gain his ends—
Assisted by his wriggly friends.
The eels had planned the coming week
To have a party in the Creek;
And there a hundred eels or more
Were polishing the ball-room floor;
And Bill engaged them, for a fee,
To take the packing box to sea.
With wise and systematic plan
He had arranged his caravan:
And every eel that evening knew
Exactly what he had to do.
So when the fox as usual made
His visit to the barricade,
Bill, through a knot-hole, gaily cried:
"Fat ducks live on the other side!

THE DUCK'S DEVICE—*Continued*

Across the river very far,
I saw a fatter duck than Ma,
And heard her talking with a goose
Of some new method to reduce."
"Good news indeed!" the fox replied,
"How does one reach the other side?"
Bill said, to show his approbation,
He would arrange for transportation,
And through the knot-hole told the fox,
Exactly where to find the box.
"And when you find it, give a cough,"
Bill said,   "And I will push you off."
"All right, " replied the fox, "I will."
Thinking he'd make a meal of Bill.
But when he coughed, Bill simply stayed
At home behind the barricade,
And through the knot-hole in the shack
Thrust out his head and gave a quack.
The box lay at the water's edge;
The eels lay hidden in the sedge—
Prepared to pull on with a line
As soon as Bill should give the sign.
With tails tight twisted round the cord,
Hearing the signal "All aboard,"
The eels swam seaward with the fox
Bobbing behind them in the box.
"Wait," called the fox, in some distress,

THE DUCK'S DEVICE—*Continued*

"I have not got the duck's address."
The eels replied: "We must make haste,
We have not any time to waste."
Now, when the tumbling tides come back,
To fill the Petitcodiac,
For miles and miles you hear the roar
Of the incoming tidal bore;
With rush and tumult, on it raves
Behind a frill of little waves.
The river, in this troubled state,
Looks much like boiling chocolate.
And all this figured in Bill's scheme
 To lure the fox into the stream.
For tidal waters, when they rise,
Will soon the strongest craft capsize.
The eels, when they discerned the roar,
Let go the box and swam ashore.
And waters shattering the box,
Soon made a plaything of the fox.
Excitement reigned within the shack,
When all the wriggling eels came back,
And by the moonlight's silver beam
No fox appeared upon the stream.
And all remarked in cheerful strain:
"He'll never trouble us again!"
 In recognition of the deed,
 The ducks arranged a little feed,

THE DUCK'S DEVICE—*Concluded*

And with the eels in much delight
They held high revelry that night.
Now evermore they safely quack
Beside the Petitcodiac.

MORAL:

The moral, although very true,
Will not, I hope, apply to you.
But when we do not like at all
The people who drop in to call
And with some apprehension feel
They wish us to supply a meal;
Then like the ducks, if we are wise,
We will some simple plan devise
And lure them to another shore
To be the victims of a bore.

MY GARDEN PLOT

I planted a cabbage in my garden bed.
I'm fond of the cabbage—it has a good head.

I planted potatoes in neat little rows.
Potatoes have eyes—though they haven't a nose.

I planted some corn, because it has ears,
But I didn't plant onions—they always cause tears.

My neighbour's fat rooster called out from the fence:
"The grubs in your garden are simply immense!"

I answered, "Go 'way there, you greedy old scrub;
It's no place for roosters to grub for their grub!"

Said the hedgehog, who chanced to be passing just then,
"If you're writing a book, here's a quill for a pen."

I said "Thanks for the offer to lend me a quill,
I'd like to accept, but I don't think I will."

The hedgehog passed on, saying: "Oh, very well,
But you make a mistake, it would make your book sell."

The pigs from the farmyard then started to squeal,
They would give me their pen for a measure of meal.

A frog, with a voice that was just like a sneeze,
Said: "I want to be put in your book, if you please."

MY GARDEN PLOT—*Concluded*

I said to the frog, "What on earth can you do
To induce me to write of a creature like you?"

He answered quite rudely: "You silly old thing,
I conduct the most notable concerts of spring!"

Then the peacock called, saying, "I hope you won't fail
To mention my beautiful tail in your tale."

I said to the creatures, "I wish you'd be still,
You clamour as though I were making my will!

"I shall finish my story right here on the spot,
And depend on my garden to furnish the plot."

It might have been better, but then it is brief,
Besides there's no moral and that's a relief.

THE OLD TIME SCHOOL

The schoolhouse of the olden time
    (So aged people say)
Was not at all the kind of school
    That you attend to-day.

It was a building made of logs
    (As often I've been told)
Which was in summer very hot,
    In winter freezing cold.

For children of the Loyalists,
    It was the general rule,
To wander through primeval woods,
    Upon their way to school.

And oftentimes they'd meet a wolf
    Or sometimes meet a bear.
An Indian with a tomahawk
    Was neither here nor there.

Now what would those dear children say,
    Who walked to school so far,
Could they have rolled up to the door,
    In Father's motor car?

Their teacher was an aged man,
    Who wore a black skull cap,
And punished all offending ones,
    With a resounding strap.

And oftentimes they'd meet a wolf
Or sometimes meet a bear.

THE OLD TIME SCHOOL—*Continued*

And well he taught such useful things
    As how to read and spell;
Their writing looked like copperplate,
    They learned to write so well.

He taught the children all to work
    (They never thought of play).
A holiday was quite unknown
    Except on Christmas day.

But could they see the lovely school
    That you attend to-day;
With all the comforts you enjoy—
    I wonder what they'd say?

And yet you often hear it said
    (And grandmothers agree)
That children now are not as good
    As once they used to be.

MORAL:

And now you cannot fail to see,
    How all their faults were cured,
Just by the things they did not have,
    And hardships they endured.
Then never fail to keep in mind

THE OLD TIME SCHOOL—*Concluded*

Those darling little pets,
Dressed in their funny frocks and caps,
Kerchiefs and pantalettes.
And don't avoid unpleasant things,
And some day you may say:
"Ah, children now are not as good,
As they were in my day!"

TOO MUCH SEA

If I could go a-sailing, a-sailing up and down,
I'd keep on sailing till I came in sight of London Town.
And when I got to London, I'd find my way about,
And wait outside the palace door to see the king ride out.

The king goes out a-riding, with trappings all of gold,
And prancing steeds and banners bright like fairy tale
      of old;
With princes and princesses and knights and ladies gay,
And trumpeters a-trumpeting "The king rides out to-
      day!"

The king is dressed in velvet and wears a golden crown,
His cloak is all of ermine and crimson is his gown.
And if he chanced to see me, I wonder if he'd say:
"I see a little stranger child among the crowds to-day."

If I could sail to London (and how I wish I could)
I'd leave the little clearing within the maple wood.
I'd leave the baby rabbit that plays about the lane.
I don't think I'd be home-sick for I'd come home again.

I'd have to cross the ocean that lies beyond the Bay.
I fear the town of London is very far away.
I'd like to sail to London, but that can never be,
I cannot sail to London because of too much sea.

If I could sail to London (and how I wish I could)

TOO MUCH SEA—*Concluded*

Supposing it might happen (although it never could)
The king should come a-riding into our maple wood.
Suppose the sea was empty and he came riding down,
With all his gay attendants, far out from London town.

Supposing in the Autumn there could be such a thing;
Our clearing is a splendid place for welcoming a king.
The maples all are crimson, and gold the aspen tree,
With silver birch a royal sight for any king to see.

And if I should be playing within the woodland wild,
The king himself might find me and say, "Come hither,
  child."
But that is just supposing, for it could never be:
No king could ride from London, because of too much
  sea.

But sometimes I'll be thinking, when I am all alone,
How much a king would have to know, who reigns upon
  a throne?
I wonder if by chance he knows (I don't suppose he
  could),
That far across the sea a child plays in a maple wood.

THE ONE-EYED WARRIOR

Old Ananias is a man who lives down by the shore.
He often tells me curious things that happened in the
           war;
But when I tell these things at home, Mother says:
           "What a shame!"
And Dad says Ananias is just keeping up the name.

He claims it was the Kaiser's fault that all this war befell.
He blames him for his missing eye and forty scars as
           well.
Because the Kaiser ruled a land that did not get much
           sun,
And wished for brighter Fatherlands where he could
           have more fun.

He thought about his cousin George, who sat on
           England's throne,
Peacefully ruling pleasant lands his Grandma used to
           own,
And when he pondered on it, he grew morose and sad,
To think that George had fallen heir to all his Grand-
           ma had.

The Kaiser then made up his mind that what he wished
           to do,
Was confiscate from cousin George a colony or two.
For years he thought about it, he thought and thought
           and thought—
Then up and did some dreadful things the which he
           hadn't ought.

THE ONE-EYED WARRIOR—*Continued*

He marched his troops through Belgium, a solemn
    treaty tore,
And plunged the half of Europe in a most uncalled-for
    war.
So when they told his cousin George the havoc William
    wrought,
He said: "There are important things that William
    must be taught."

Then George put on his helmet, where he wore his
    crown before,
And quietly got off his throne and started for the
    war;
And when he saw the Kaiser ride by in armoured car,
He boldly went to meet him and said: "Ah, there you
    are!"

And then he said: "Now, William, you've made a big
    mistake;
This war is not the kind of war that Grandma used to
    make.
You have disgraced the family! You cannot have the
    sun;
Go home and rule your Fatherland the way it should
    be done."

Then William in an angry voice replied: "I vill you tell
I vant to rule mine Faderland und Mudderland as vell!"

THE ONE-EYED WARRIOR—*Continued*

But George still answered firmly: "You can't have all
      the sun—
If you *are* Grandma's grandchild, you're not the only
      one!
You will end in St. Helena, to finish up your lark,
And be glad to find a corner where it's always after
      dark."

Having said these things to William, King George went
      home again
To the pleasant land of England, where his Grandma
      used to reign.
And Ananias met him there, just walking down the
      street.
The king held out his hand and said: "How lucky that
      we meet!

"Now, Ananias, my good man, I know how brave you
      are.
I hear that you have *lost* an eye and suffered many a
      scar!
Go straightway to the battle-lines and see my troops,"
      said he:
"And make a little note of things and bring it back to
      me;
And tell my cousin William there, he'll be an exile yet.
Then ask my brave and war-like men to carry out the
      threat."

Old Ananias is a man who lives down by the shore.
He often tells me curious things that happened in the war;

THE ONE-EYED WARRIOR—*Concluded*

So Ananias went of course (what else was there to do?)
And after fighting long and hard, he made the threat
    come true.
And now he's home without an eye and forty scars or
    more—
And yet I've never heard him say 'twas he that won
    the war!

But when I tell my mother this, she says, "Oh, little son,
I think that Ananias was saying that in fun!"
But Dad, you know, was at the war and knows it
    through and through
And he says Ananias tells a heap of things that's true!

KING OF THE CASTLE

Away along the Fundy shore,
    A mile or two from town,
There is a place where, years before,
    The rocks have fallen down.

And there I play that by the sea
    I own a castle grand,
And there I reign in majesty
    And wisely rule the land.

My court yard is this open space;
    My banquet hall that square;
My armoury and council place
    Are up that rocky stair.

Down in the dungeons grievously
    My prisoners lament;
And I go down and set them free,
    As soon as they repent.

High up the cliff, where roses fair
    Grow far as you can see,
A lovely princess stays up there
    And weaves her tapestry.

And when a boat with sails of white
    Comes sailing on the Bay

So when I see the sun decline,
My sad farewells are said,
And off I go to Palestine
Upon a last Crusade.

KING OF THE CASTLE—*Continued*

I say: "Behold, ye gallant knight,
    What frigate comes this way?"

Some royal guest may visit soon
    My castle by the sea,
Prepare the feast and trumpets tune
    To merry minstrelsy!

And when marauding pirates come,
    I have them in my power.
A thousand archers shoot at them
    From battlement and tower.

But, when the poor and the oppressed
    Come to my castle door,
I open up my treasure chest
    And give them of its store.

I play our history book again,
    As far as we have gone,
That's nearly all of Richard's reign,
    And almost up to John.

So when I see the sun decline,
    My sad farewells are said,
And off I go to Palestine
    Upon a last Crusade.

KING OF THE CASTLE—*Concluded*

The greatest king in all the land,
    What wealth or power has he
Like kingdoms at a child's command,
    In castles by the sea?

COMING HOME TO QUODDY

Oh, Quoddy of the Islands,
    Oh, Quoddy of the sea!
Our white prow cuts the waters—
    And I'm coming back to thee.

Oh, Quoddy of the herring weir
    And shoal and sandy bar!
I'm sailing back to you again
    From distant lands afar.

Oh, Quoddy in the city streets,
    There are no birds to sing,
No blackberries in Autumn,
    No Mayflowers in Spring!

Oh, Quoddy where the sunbeams dance,
    Upon the whitecap's foam!
I'm dancing with the dancing waves
    Upon the journey home.

Oh, Quoddy in my little room,
    My toys are on the floor!
My books are on the cupboard shelf
    And some are in the drawer.

Oh, Quoddy, when the swallows build
    Beneath the stable eaves,
I'm sure to find a robin's nest
    Among the lilac leaves!

COMING HOME TO QUODDY—*Concluded*

Oh, Quoddy of the fir trees,
　　Where winds the Indian trail,
I'm watching for your rocky shores
　　Beyond the steamer's rail!

Oh, Quoddy of the Islands,
　　When land appears in sight,
There'll be a little child on board
　　That's strangled with delight!

Oh, Quoddy of the Islands,
　　Oh, Quoddy of the Sea,
Oh, don't you know a happy child
　　Is sailing back to thee!

SPINNING WHEEL SONG*

When safely the harvest is stored in the barn,
   'Tis then we make ready for spinning the yarn;
When summer is over and winter is near,
    The song of the wheel is the sound that you hear.
    Oh, this is the song that the spinning wheel sings:
    "You soon will need mufflers and mittens and things,
    So draw a long thread with each turn of the wheel
    And double and twist it with spindle and reel!"

When flowers are faded and swallows are fled
   And trees on the hillsides are yellow and red.
When mornings are frosty and evenings are long,
   'Tis then we will sing you our spinning wheel song.
    Oh, this is the song that the spinning wheel sings:
    "You soon will need mufflers and mittens and things,
    So draw a long thread with each turn of the wheel
    And double and twist it with spindle and reel!"

Soon over the mountains the snow-drifts will come,
   And settle down deep by the door of our home.
With mufflers and mittens, how warm we shall feel
   And value the yarn that was spun on the wheel.
    Oh, this is the song that the spinning wheel sings:
    "You soon will need mufflers and mittens and things,
    So draw a long thread with each turn of the wheel
    And double and twist it with spindle and reel·"

*Written for the Farmers' Pageant.

6

THE SAND REEF LIGHT

The lighthouse on the sand reef is like a friend to me,
That sends out little friendly beams across the twilight
    sea.
Beyond the distant seine-reel, beyond the herring weir,
When day draws on to evening, I see its light appear.

When winds through bird-forsaken trees and leafless
    branches sound,
When damp and dead the garden growth lies rotting
    on the ground,
When early autumn shadows fall across the wind-swept
    sea,
I watch to see the Sand Reef send out its light for me.

When crows from barren stubble fields fly home against
    the sky,
When from the lonely tracts of sand, I hear the sea-
    gulls cry,
I stand beside the window, till through the gathering
    night,
I catch again the friendly gleam of my lone Sand Reef
    light.

When dark and strange on moonless nights the hills
    and valleys lie,
With many far mysterious stars inhabiting the sky,
Apart from those too numerous lights that fill the seas
    of space,
My little human earthly star shines in a lower place.

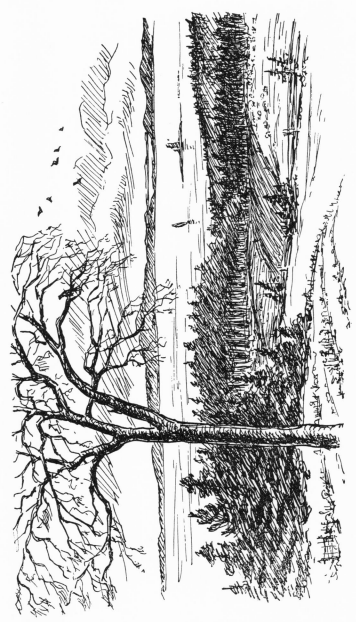

The lighthouse on the sand reef is like a friend to me,
That sends out little friendly beams across the twilight sea.

THE SAND REEF LIGHT—*Continued*

When broken-hearted winter storms come howling
    down the lane,
Beating the frozen creeper boughs against the window
    pane,
When depths of darkness have engulfed the earth and
    sky and sea,
I hope that storms will never hide that little light from
    me.

The twinkling of its cheerful ray lights me through
    drifting snow,
To pleasant thoughts of yesterday and lands I loved
    to know.
I know the rocky ledges, where the sea-gull nests in
    spring,
And clefts among the sand-stone rocks where slender
    hairbells cling.

Through flower-scented summer nights I watch its
    tiny star
Guide home belated fishing boats to moorings on the
    bar.
I watch its light go out again when morning dawn
    reveals
The island homes of nesting gulls, the playgrounds of
    the seals.

It waits for little fishing boats to bring their spoils from sea
And I wait for another child to come and play with me.

THE SAND REEF LIGHT—*Concluded*

We watch and wait together, the sand reef light and I,
As waits the drift of yesterday the ebb of bye-and-bye.
It waits for little fishing boats to bring their spoils
    from sea
And I wait for another child to come and play with me.

AT BED TIME

The sun when he grows weary,
    He tumbles into bed,
He leaves the hillside dreary,
    He leaves the sky-line red.

Up from the pasture-land I hear
    A bleating mother sheep
Telling her baby lamb, "My dear,
    It's time you went to sleep."

Within the forest I can tell
    That deep in every nest,
With sleepy chirp the birds as well
    Have settled down to rest.

And in the ponds are father frogs,
    Who stay awake to sing
Melodies to the pollywogs,
    Through the long nights of spring.

Along the shore the murmuring sea
    Calls home the little waves,
That hide themselves mischievously
    Among dark rocks and caves.

And to my bed, all pink and white,
I take my baby dear—

AT BED TIME—*Concluded*

And through my open window,
　　The sweetest scents are shed,
From hawthorn in the hedgerow
　　And the narcissus bed.

And to my bed, all pink and white,
　　I take my baby dear—
And tell her stories in the night
　　About the sounds we hear.

THE OLD GARDEN
(*A Remembrance*)

When I was a little child, many years away,
In a pleasant garden place once I used to play—
Taken there in summer time and left to spend the day.

I can see the Lady of that garden rare,
Always wheeled about the walks in a garden chair
By a quiet serving-maid who waited on her there.

Here I have her portrait, hanging in the hall;
When I sit alone with it as the shadows fall,
I can see the garden—I can see it all.

Like the scent of rose-leaves by the breeze diffused,
Like the faded colours that the artist used,
I can see the garden in a dream confused.

From those years there come to me recollections sweet
Of a shaded corner in a quiet street,
And a lilac sheltered lawn where children used to meet.

Pleasant are the memories childhood years can give;
Here again I find them, subtly fugitive,
In a house behind the trees, where she used to live.

THE OLD GARDEN—*Continued*

There I see the flowers that we used to pick;
Tall white roses blooming by the sun-warmed brick—
Honey-suckle hanging, where the bees came thick.

There I see the children, children everywhere,
And the sweet Acacias perfuming the air:
And I myself a little child among the children there.

Spring would bring narcissus, summer hollyhocks,
Sweet syringa blossoms and fragrant beds of stocks,
Ribbon grass and bleeding-heart and great tall clumps
        of phlox.

In the kitchen garden, through the picket fence,
Red translucent currants hung in clusters dense.
Mint and herbs and parsley shed their wholesome scents.

I can see the croquet lawns, where the ladies played,
Every pleasant afternoon, in the lilac shade.
I can hear the tapping by their mallets made.

I can see the children running down the walk,
Bearing as a banner a giant rhubarb stalk,
Echoes of old fairy tales lingering in their talk.

When the changeful shadows on the grass grew long,
Every day the church bell rang for evensong—
Shrill into the summer air its silver notes would throng:

*I can see the croquet lawns where the ladies
    played,
Every pleasant afternoon, in the lilac shade,
I can hear the tapping by their mallets made.*

THE OLD GARDEN—*Concluded*

Ringing in the tower of the church across the way.
We could watch the people going in to pray,
See the white-haired rector hurry on his way.

Listening in the covert of the lilac trees,
We could hear the people rising from their knees,
And solemn organ tones roll down in holy harmonies.

All the flower sweetness of that garden place,
All the tranquil loveliness, all the gentle grace
Lingers in the portrait of this quiet face.

I can see a little child taken home again
Where the sunset lingers like a crimson stain;
I can hear the waggon wheels coming down the lane—
No! It was the lonely wind that shook the window
        pane!

        Now to all little children,
                In farewell I would say:
        Never forget the gardens
                Where you have loved to play!